How to use this book

Follow the advice, in italics, given for you on each page.

Support the children as they read the text that is shaded in cream.

Praise *the children at every step!*

Detailed guidance is provided in the Read Write Inc. Phonics Handbook

9 reading activities

Children:

Practise reading the speed sounds.

Read the green, red and challenge words for the story.

Listen as you read the introduction.

Discuss the vocabulary check with you.

Read the story.

Re-read the story and discuss the 'questions to talk about'.

Read the story with fluency and expression.

Answer the questions to 'read and answer'.

Practise reading the speed words.

Speed sounds

Consonants
Say the pure sounds (do not add 'uh').

f ff	l ll (le)	m mm (mb)	n nn kn	r rr (wr)	s ss (se)	v ve	z zz s	sh	th	ng nk

b bb	c k (ck)	d dd	g gg	h	j	p pp	qu	t tt	w wh	x	y	ch (tch)

Vowels
Say the sounds in and out of order.

at	hen head	in	on	up	day	see happy	high find	blow no

zoo	look	car	for door snore	fair	whirl	shout	boy spoil

*Each box contains one sound but sometimes more than one grapheme. Focus graphemes are **circled**.*

Green words

ni**gh**t   <u>ou</u>t   **sh** <u>ow</u>   h<u>ea</u>d   litt le   lun**ch**

w<u>oo</u>d   g<u>oo</u>d   l<u>oo</u>k   t<u>oo</u>k   f<u>oo</u>d   m<u>oo</u>d   st<u>oo</u>l   t<u>oo</u>   pr<u>oo</u>f   sm<u>oo</u> **th**

r<u>oo</u>f   t<u>oo</u> **th**   s<u>oo</u>n   g<u>oo</u> se   f<u>oo</u>l   **wr**ist

---

a`lo**ng**   →   alo**ng**              kit**ch**`en   →   kit**ch**en

na`**rr**ow   →   na**rr**ow          b<u>ee</u>t`root   →   b<u>ee</u>troot

ba**th**`room   →   ba**th**r<u>oo</u>m       moon`light   →   moonli**gh**t

br<u>oo</u>m`sti**ck**   →   br<u>oo</u>msti**ck**   bed`room   →   bedr<u>oo</u>m

mu**sh**`room   →   mu**sh**r<u>oo</u>m     sat`in   →   satin

---

pu**sh**   →   pu**sh**ed   scr<u>ee</u>**ch**   →   scr<u>ee</u>**ch**ed   c<u>oo</u>k   →   c<u>oo</u>ked

sc<u>oo</u>p   →   sc<u>oo</u>ped   f<u>oo</u>l   →   f<u>oo</u>led

5

Red words

wh<u>ere</u> s<u>ome</u> <u>they</u> was <u>you</u> s<u>ai</u>d to be <u>she</u>
w<u>ere</u> <u>th</u><u>ere</u> go <u>are</u> my ta<u>ll</u> ca<u>ll</u> wa<u>ll</u>*

Challenge words

supp<u>er</u>   salt   oven

*Red word for this story only

The foolish witch

Introduction

Do you know the story of Hansel and Gretel? They were children lost in a wood. Starving hungry they found a house made of sweets and toffee. How would you feel? A witch calls them in and offers them delicious food and somewhere to stay. Would you stay with a witch?

What do you think will happen to them?

Story written by Gill Munton

Illustrated by Tim Archbold

Vocabulary check

Discuss the meaning (as used in the story) after the children have read each word.

	definition:	sentence:
sobbing	crying	Sobbing, they set off...
log cabin	a small wooden house	Hansel and Gretel began to munch on bits of cabin.
scooping	picking	Gretel, scooping up the crumbs.
gloomy	dark and miserable	She flung Hansel into the gloomy hut.
clumpy	big and heavy	The witch put on her clumpy boots.
stooped	bent over	The witch stooped down.
quick as a flash	very, very fast	Quick as a flash, Gretel pushed her in.

Punctuation to note in this story:
1. Capital letters to start sentences and full stop to end sentences
2. Capital letters for names
3. Exclamation marks to show anger, shock and surprise
4. 'Wait and see' dots...

The foolish witch

Hansel and Gretel were lost in the wood.

Sobbing, they set off along a narrow path below the tall trees.

Soon, Hansel called, "Look, Gretel! A log cabin!"

But the walls were not logs – they were gooey toffee!

The windows were not glass, but sweets!

Hansel and Gretel began to munch on bits of cabin.

"Mmm! The roof is the best bit!" said Gretel,

scooping up the crumbs.

But just then, a head popped out of the bathroom window.

A tall black hat, a spotty chin, a long, yellow tooth …

It was a witch!

"You look hungry, my poppets!" she screeched.

"Let me give you some food,

and I will give you a bed for the night, too!"

So Hansel and Gretel had a very good supper,

a fat goose with fresh mushrooms and beetroot.

That night, in a sweet little
bedroom with a clock on the wall,
they slept on soft beds, with
smooth satin sheets.

"She must be a good witch!" Hansel said to Gretel as they lay
in the moonlight.

But she was not.

The next day, she was in a very bad mood. She flung
Hansel into the gloomy hut where she kept her broomstick.

"Stay there until you are good and fat!" she screeched.
"Then I will cook you, and have you for lunch!"

"As for you," she said, prodding
Gretel in the chest with her thumb,
"go into the kitchen! Off you go, shoo!
We are going to feed Hansel up!"

So Gretel sat on a stool and cooked bread, and buns, and milk puddings. The witch put on her clumpy boots and took the food to the hut, pushing it in at the window.

But Hansel fooled the witch. When she asked to feel his wrist, as proof that he was getting fat, he stuck a twig out of the window. The witch felt the twig.

"Too thin, too thin!" she screeched.
"But I will still cook you for my lunch!"

She dragged Hansel into the kitchen.

She looked at Gretel, spooning salt into the pot.

"I will cook you, as well! Get into the oven!"

"I will fool the witch, too," said Gretel to herself.

To the witch she said, "I can't get in!
You must show me the best way to do it!"

So the witch stooped, and stuck her head into the oven. Quick as a flash, Gretel pushed her from behind so that she fell right in.

Gretel grinned as she slammed the oven shut.

She called to Hansel and they ran, and ran, and ran,

right away from the cabin in the woods and the wicked, wicked witch.

Questions to talk about

Re-read the page. Read the question to the children. Tell them whether it is a **FIND IT** question or **PROVE IT** question.

FIND IT

✓ Turn to the page

✓ Read the question

✓ Find the answer

PROVE IT

✓ Turn to the page

✓ Read the question

✓ Find your evidence

✓ Explain why

Page 9:	PROVE IT	What was strange about the house Hansel and Gretel saw?
Page 10:	FIND IT	What did the witch offer to do for Hansel and Gretel?
Page 11:	PROVE IT	Why did Hansel and Gretel think the witch was a good witch?
Page 12:	PROVE IT	How had the witch changed by morning?
Page 13:	PROVE IT	Why did Hansel push a twig out of the window?
Page 14:	PROVE IT	How did Gretel trick the witch?
Page 15:	PROVE IT	What do you think happened to the witch? Why do you think the story is called 'The foolish witch'?

Questions to read and answer

(Children complete without your help.)

1. The walls were **logs / wood / toffee**.

2. Gretel said that the **roof / window / door** was the best bit.

3. The witch flung Hansel into **a gloomy hut / a deep pond / a small bedroom**.

4. The witch put on a **big black hat / clumpy boots / a red dress**.

5. The witch wanted to **help / cook / play with** Hansel.

Speed words

Children practise reading the words across the rows, down the columns and in and out of order clearly and quickly.

woods	below	little	asked	cooked
windows	tooth	smooth	stooped	bedroom
too	boots	where	said	my
herself	into	were	going	there